My STORY
BLOGS BY FOUR MILITARY TEENS

Michelle D. Sherman, Ph.D. ★ DeAnne M. Sherman

Seeds of Hope Books™
...Where families matter

BEAVER'S
POND
PRESS

ISBN 10: 1-59298-303-0
ISBN 13: 978-1-59298-303-2

Library of Congress Catalog Number: 2009934801

Printed in the United States of America

First Printing: 2009
Second Printing: 2010
Third Printing: 2012

15 14 13 12   6 5 4 3

Cover and interior design by James Monroe Design, LLC.

Beaver's Pond Press, Inc.
7108 Ohms Lane
Edina, MN 55439–2129
(952) 829-8818
www.BeaversPondPress.com

BEAVER'S
POND
PRESS

To order, visit www.SeedsofHopeBooks.com
or call (800) 901-3480 x118. Special sales discounts available.

To our heroes: The children in military families.
We recognize your sacrifices and honor your courage.

Mariah

Adam

Carlos

Meredith

WELCOME

Welcome to the lives of four teenagers whose parents are in the military. Although these four youth are fictional, the stories are real—the blogs are a compilation of real life experiences of military teens we have been honored to meet. Here you will find blogs by Mariah, Adam, Carlos, and Meredith, which describe their feelings and experiences as military teens. You will read about their joy, fear, confusion, pride, and anger—and how they got through the tough times before, during, and after their parents' deployment.

As the wars in the Middle East continue, many of our service members are experiencing long and repeated deployments. Having your parent halfway around the world in a combat zone for a long time can be tough on everybody. *My Story: Blogs by Four Military Teens* was written specifically for YOU, military youth, to honor and recognize your unique joys and sacrifices, address your fears and hopes, and explore how your parents' deployment is affecting your lives.

Although every military family is unique, you've got a lot in common with other teens whose parents have been deployed in this war. As you read these blogs, we hope you will relate to some of the feelings and situations that come up in Mariah's, Adam's, Carlos' and Meredith's lives.

NOTE:

Reading about these military teens may spark some feelings in you as you think about your own family's experience. After hearing about Mariah, Adam, Carlos, and Meredith, you may wish to get some support in coping with your personal situation. Our book, *Finding My Way: A Teen's Guide to Living with a Parent Who Has Experienced Trauma*, is filled with information, activities, and exercises to help you sort through and deal with your unique experiences. If you think *Finding My Way* may be useful to you, please turn to page 52 to learn more.

Mariah

Two sisters: Destiny (11), and Sasha (5)

Mom is in the Army National Guard

Interests: Running, baking, reading magazines,
listening to music, hanging out with friends

JUNE 17

Off to War

Two weeks to go until Mom leaves for Iraq and everybody is feeling the
stress. Mom is in the Army National Guard, and I never really thought
much about being a "military family." She would just do her weekend
drill and a summer camp, and that's it. I've known about the war, but
didn't think it would ever be something that I had to worry about. Well,
she got her orders about a month ago and she's getting ready to leave.
Everything is pretty confusing right now—Mom and Dad have lots of
paperwork and business to take care of. I get scared when I think of her
leaving. We're pretty close and I talk to her about everything. Dad's great
but it's not the same. It freaks me out sometimes thinking about Mom
being so far away....

I'm going to make a card for Mom and hide it in her duffel bag. I want
to tell her how proud I am and how much I love her. She can keep it by
her bed (or maybe she'll sleep on a cot in the barracks over there, I don't
know). I'm going to include my favorite picture of us from our camping
trip last summer—I know it will make her cry. I sure hope we can keep in

1

touch by email and that we can talk once in a while…I just want to be able to hear her voice.

My First 5k Race

Ran my first ever 5k race yesterday. It was a really hot day, so I was exhausted after…but I was so pumped to have finished and got a cool race t-shirt. My dad and sisters were at the finish line cheering me on which was sweet. The race was a fundraiser for the cancer unit at the local children's hospital, so it was for a good cause. Getting up WAY too early on a Saturday morning was worth it. I made pretty good time, and bet I'll be even faster at the next race in a couple weeks (hopefully it will be cooler!). My legs are SO sore today—ugh!!

Iraq—The Other Side of the World

Mom has been gone for two months now—we're doing OK but still trying to figure out who does what chores and how Destiny, Sasha, and I can get to all our practices, games, and school stuff. Before Mom left we had a couple family activities—a short camping trip and a movie night. It was fun but…I really miss Mom. It's so different without her.

Sometimes I can't watch TV when they show bombs, people getting hurt, and lots of homes and buildings being destroyed. It keeps me up at night—I have nightmares. I'm terrified Mom might get really hurt or, even worse, might not come home at all—what would I do without her? I can't believe she's over there—she seems so far away and sometimes I feel really alone.

SEPTEMBER 29

Got My Ears Pierced

Got my ears double pierced at the mall last week. Now I bet Destiny will want to get hers done, too. Dad's not happy, but I think it looks cool. Maybe I'll surprise him with a nose ring some day. ☺

OCTOBER 15

Military Group

Joined a military group at school. Our school counselor, Mr. Rodriguez, organized it and we meet about once a month. I even get to get out of math class to go to group. There are 12 kids and we all have parents who are or have been in Iraq or Afghanistan. We just talk about what's going on—what's hard about having a parent so far away and in danger. I haven't said anything yet, but it's OK—you don't have to talk if you don't want to. Things at home are pretty tense these days—a lot of drama and yelling. This is hard on Dad, too. I think we all miss Mom...I think I'm mad at her for leaving me....

OCTOBER 31

Halloween

Destiny and I gave out candy tonight to the trick-or-treaters. Sasha dressed up as a princess—she was so cute. It made me think a lot about Mom, though, because she loves helping us get dressed up for Halloween. Anyway...I tried out for the school play last week. I'm not much of an actress, but it helps to stay busy and it gets my mind off the war. It feels good to be thinking about something else...but sometimes I feel guilty that she's off at war and I'm doing fun stuff....

Our military group at school is having a fundraiser. We're selling candy and using the money to put together care packages to send to Iraq.

This is a pretty cool project, and I feel like I fit in with the other kids. Mr. Rodriguez is a good guy—he's a veteran himself so he really understands us and what we're going through. He tells us to stay positive and have a good attitude. I'm trying—but sometimes it's hard.

NOVEMBER 2

Phone Call from the "Sandbox"

Mom called again today—at first it was really hard, not at all like how we used to talk. I didn't know what to say. There are so many things I want to talk to her about—I need her help and she's so far away! I told her I got my ears pierced and that I made the school play. Really stinks she'll miss my show. Dad will record it and my grandparents will be there, but it just won't be the same. It ended up being a good conversation. It just felt good to hear her voice again.

NOVEMBER 20

School Play

I had a lot of fun with our school play. After practicing for so long, it was great to finally have an audience who laughed at the funny lines. Dad, Destiny, and Sasha brought me flowers. I miss Mom. Sometimes I cry a lot—usually in my bedroom at night. I hate having to baby-sit Sasha and do all the extra chores at home—Mom always did the laundry and dishes, but now I have to. This is really getting old. I'm lonely, angry, and scared—sometimes it's bad—very bad—worse than awful.

DECEMBER 5

New Kids in Military Group

Destiny and I made some chocolate chip cookies last weekend—Sasha wanted to help, but she just made a mess and ate the raw cookie dough! I brought a plate of cookies to military group on Wednesday—they were a big hit. A couple new kids in our school came for the first time—they seemed kind of shy like I was in the beginning. One girl named Kim is in my math class so we can go together. I think she needs a friend to help get comfortable with the other kids. I can tell she really misses her dad. The other new person is a guy named Elijah. His older brother just joined the Navy and left for boot camp. His whole family is nervous about the war. Elijah is really close to his brother—calls him his "hero." Elijah seems so scared and lonely. He misses hanging out with his brother and worries a lot. You never expect your big brother to go halfway around the world to fight in a war.

DECEMBER 27

Sasha Talks to Santa

We took Sasha to see Santa at the mall. Instead of asking for toys, she asked Santa to send Mom home. That made me cry. I want Mom back, too. Christmas Day was really different this year. Usually we have people over to our house…instead we went to my Aunt Linda's place. It was nice but weird without Mom. Everybody is trying to make up for Mom being gone. I miss her so much.

FEBRUARY 5

Kim's Birthday

Had fun at Kim's birthday party. She had a sleep-over and we gave each other manicures, watched movies, and texted some guys from school all night. Her parents thought we were sleeping.

MARCH 10

Spent Spring Break in Bed!

Got really sick with strep throat, so spent my whole Spring Break in bed—yuck! Dad took good care of me—got me magazines and popsicles—but I missed Mom and her homemade chicken noodle soup. Sasha and I played games and watched a lot of movies. After awhile that got boring. Feeling better now—just in time to head back to school. Great timing....

APRIL 18

Checking off the Days

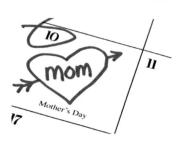

New neighbors just moved in and they have two kids. They asked me to baby-sit which is perfect because I need the money. This deployment thing is getting really long—Mom's been gone 9 months now and she's missing so much of my life. There's a mother-daughter lunch at church for Mother's Day next month—it really stinks that I have no one to go with.

Destiny, Sasha, and I can really get sad, and Dad is always so busy. He gets mad about stuff and I get fed up with him—so my sisters and I just go to our rooms and listen to music. We're counting the days until Mom gets home—it seems like forever! One good thing—I get to tell my sisters what to do. I'm in charge when Dad is at work—I like that....

MAY 14

Hanging Out at the Mall

Going shopping for new clothes and earrings tonight—babysitting money is awesome! Kim and I are getting to be good friends, and we talk about being military kids. It's nice to be able to talk to someone who really understands. We talk to some of our other friends, too—some understand, some don't. Some can't even find Iraq and Afghanistan on the map—they're so clueless. Oh well. I ended up going to the mother-daughter lunch after all. My Aunt Linda went with me, and we really had fun. I told her how much I miss Mom—it felt good to open up to her. I know she can't wait for her sister to get home, too.

I still like going to military group (sure beats math!). Mr. Rodriguez talked to us about how President Obama and his wife Michelle are really trying to help military families—in fact, it's one of Michelle's main things to do while she's first lady...very cool.

AUGUST 13

Can't Wait to See Mom!

I cannot believe Mom will be home in a few days. I'm SO excited! We're cleaning the house like crazy. They've changed the homecoming date a few times which has been driving me insane. It's been a little over a year. Buses will bring all the soldiers to the armory downtown. There will be a group of us going to meet her, including Grandma and Grandpa. They've really missed Mom, too. We're gonna make Welcome Home signs. I'm actually pretty nervous about seeing her. I'm not sure what to wear. Will she look the same? Will she notice how I've grown? Will she like my new haircut? How will we get along? I've changed so much, and Mom has been gone for a long time—I'm worried we won't be as close as we were before. This is really awkward. I'm so nervous, but I can't wait to see my mom.

AUGUST 18

"New Normal?"

The Welcome Home event was a blast. As soon as I saw Mom we hugged and cried, and everything was great. There were lots of people—music, speeches, activities, and tons of food. Now we're all home as a family of five. It feels good to be together but everything has to be changed around again. Nothing seems normal. Nothing is the way it was before Mom left, or while she was gone (I can't boss Destiny and Sasha around anymore). Mom and Dad tell us we need to find a "new normal"—a new way of getting along after a parent returns home from war. Mom is the one who left—why do WE have to do all the changing? Why can't we just be regular like some of my friends? Sometimes I'm jealous that they don't have to deal with all of this....

NOVEMBER 26

I'm Stuffed!

Just finished a big turkey dinner. Like we do every Thanksgiving, we went around the table and said what we are thankful for (I said "having Mom home"). Mom started talking about Iraq and how thankful she was to be home. Then she kind of opened up about all the good stuff that happened when she was over there—how she gave candy to a lot of Iraqi children

and how her unit helped to rebuild schools and sports centers…and how thankful the Iraqi people were. This was pretty cool because she'd never talked about what they did over there before. A really different Thanksgiving—I'll always remember it….

FEBRUARY 21

Family of Five Again

Mom's been home six months now, and I guess it's going OK. It's still hard to understand everything. We all changed when Mom was gone and now we are trying to get close as a family again. This may take a while. Even though it's good to be together again, I'm scared to death she may be sent back to Iraq. I've heard some people go back 2, 3 or even more times—I'm not sure I could handle that. It was so hard when Mom was gone the first time…I can't imagine her being gone again.

I still go to military group once in a while—I've made some friends, and I can help other kids whose parents are in the military. It feels good to help other people.

This is What I've Learned

✓ Deployment can be rough on everybody in the family, but it doesn't last forever—really!

✓ Hanging out with kids whose parents are in the military can help because they know what you're going through.

✓ It helps to stay busy and stick to a regular schedule. Doing 5k runs and being in the school play were great and helped to pass the time until Mom got home.

✓ It feels good to help other kids.

✓ It is taking time to adjust to Mom being home…it's taken longer than I thought it would because everyone has changed a lot. I guess that "new normal" phrase makes sense…we're kind of creating it as we go.

Something to think about . . .

Mariah experienced a lot of ups and downs before, during, and after her mom's deployment. Sometimes she felt sad and lonely, sometimes proud and excited, and other times angry and resentful. That's normal. As difficult as these feelings may be to identify and experience, they are all OK and common for teens whose parents deploy to a war zone. It's important not to judge your feelings, but to recognize and accept them.

Here is a list of emotions that military teens often experience. Which ones can you relate to?

Bored	**Hopeful**	**Proud**
Confused	**Hurt**	**Really down**
Depressed	**Important**	**Resentful**
Different	**Invisible**	**Strong**
Forgotten	**Left out**	**Understood**
Frustrated	**Lonely**	**Worried**
Guilty	**Numb**	**Others?**

Adam

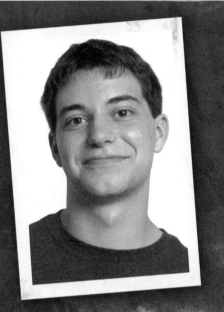

One brother (Derrick, 19) and two sisters, Ashley (14) and Lisa (9)

Dad is in the Air Force Reserves

Interests: Playing videogames, hanging out with friends, going to movies, playing soccer

....

AUGUST 20

Dad is Home...

My dad is one of the coolest, smartest, bravest men I've ever met, but sometimes I just can't stand being around him. He's a doctor—a surgeon—and is in the Air Force Reserves. He just returned from a second tour in Iraq, and he sure acts different. After his first tour, it took us some time to get caught up, but just when things got normal again, he got his orders to go back to Iraq. Now he's finally home (for good?), but he just isn't the same. He gets mad over the stupidest things and spends most of his time in his bedroom or in front of the computer. He's still in "military mode," and orders us around way too much. He doesn't joke around like before, and sometimes just hangs out in the garage by himself. We don't talk much. I almost liked it better when he was gone. It was a lot quieter and less stressful around the house. Ashley, Lisa, and I just stay out of his way. Derrick is lucky—he's leaving for college soon.

Soccer try outs are in two weeks. I need to start running to get in shape.

SEPTEMBER 4

I Can't Have the Car??

Derrick left for college—he was pretty excited to get out of here. I don't blame him. Sometimes I wish I could go, too. My dad and I got into a huge fight last night. I wanted the car to go out with some friends and he wouldn't let me have it. What's going on? I've had my license for 6 months and I drive everywhere. Dad just doesn't get it. Things happened while he was away, and he hasn't caught up with our lives yet. He treats me like a little kid. It's like all he cares about is himself. I hate the way he wants to control me! I don't know what I did to make him so mad, but he sure went off on me.

I've got a big algebra test tomorrow. I can't concentrate on anything. I made the soccer team. It's good to have something to look forward to and the coach is great.

SEPTEMBER 28

What Is Up with Dad?

I've got a big soccer tournament and Dad says he's not coming—some lame excuse about too many people, too much noise, and he can't handle the traffic. Mom will be there, though—that's good. I really cannot believe Dad is not coming. He's quiet and so nervous now—the littlest thing totally freaks him out. Just last week Ashley and Lisa were playing cards—Slap Jack—on the kitchen table, and Dad came unglued. The sound of them slapping the table really set him off, and he yelled at my sisters. I kinda felt badly for them, so I took them out for ice cream later that night.

IED = Improvised Explosive Device – also called a roadside bomb

Anyway, I wish I could have some friends over to the house but I think it would be embarrassing. I never know how Dad is going to act. This stinks.

Dad doesn't sleep much and sometimes I can hear him walking around at night. I try not to ride in the car with him because he drives crazy (and they think I am a bad driver? Whatever!). Dad sometimes swerves all over if he sees any trash or garbage bags. I guess it's because he had to avoid stuff that could have been an IED in Iraq.

Oh yeah, I hate to say this, but I think he's been drinking a lot lately. I see lots of beer cans in the recycling—sometimes he's just a zombie— maybe it's because he's not sleeping at night.

I'm driving again—finally!

OCTOBER 10

PTSD???

Things have changed a lot around here. Dad has started going to the VA hospital—it seems like he goes up there for appointments all the time. I've driven by that big hospital lots of times but

PTSD = Post-Traumatic Stress Disorder

never thought MY dad would go there! The doctors say Dad has PTSD. Guess that's from trying to save so many wounded troops. That's basically all he did in Iraq. He saw so much bad stuff over there that it got to him. I had no idea! He thinks about all the people he operated on and wonders how many lived or died. He says he can't get those images out of his head. He dreams about it and says he sees it all over again when he closes his eyes.

The docs at the VA are really helpful—they have special programs for vets with PTSD. His therapist says that emotional wounds are just as serious as physical wounds, and that we can all help Dad by being patient and supportive. Sometimes that's hard to do!

OCTOBER 22

Soccer Starter

Dad is still seeing a therapist for his PTSD. Dealing with all the crap he saw in Iraq is tough, but he really wants to get his life back. Like I said, he's one of the coolest, smartest, bravest men I ever met and I've never been more proud of him. He says he still can't come to my soccer games—even though I'm disappointed, I understand. I used to think he was being a total jerk, but now I'm starting to understand a little better what he's going through. Hopefully he can come to a game soon because I'm starting at center forward and we're undefeated!

NOVEMBER 7

Grounded...What the Heck?

Got grounded for staying out past curfew. That's all I need is more time in my house. At least I can talk to my friends on Facebook and play video-games. Soccer ended a couple weeks ago—had a great season and I played a lot. Dad did make it to one game—that meant a lot to me.

DECEMBER 6

Making Progress

Dad is doing better. The VA hospital really helps—he goes to some group up there every week where he talks with other veterans from Iraq and Afghanistan. They talk about stuff I don't understand, but he usually feels better afterward. Dad and I are getting closer, too—he's even talking about buying me a car. I'm so psyched!

Last week I had a couple friends over to watch movies. Dad came downstairs and hung out with us for a while—that's a real change from how he was when he first got home.

Dad is trying to get back to work and is doing some surgery again—just a couple times a week. I can tell he feels good about that. Things are getting back to normal at home, too, but he's still pretty quiet. We've been shooting hoops in the driveway like we used to. Of course, I still beat him!

Haven't seen as many beer cans in the recycling bin lately. I think that's a good sign.

DECEMBER 28

Not a "Merry Christmas"

Had Christmas at our house—great to have Derrick home. He loves college. The holidays went OK overall, but there were a few awkward moments when all the relatives came over. Dad spent most of the day in his bedroom. It was too loud and too many people. It was like his body was with us, but his mind was somewhere else.

The day ended on a good note, though, when Mom and Dad surprised me with keys to a car. Can't believe they bought me a car! I can finally be independent....

JANUARY 10

Out to Breakfast

Cut class this morning and went out to breakfast with a couple friends. So glad we didn't get caught. It was so easy—we have to do this more often! It's awesome having my own car.

JANUARY 20

Family Military Weekend

My parents, sisters, and I just got back from a Family Military Weekend at a big hotel downtown. My sisters spent most of the time in the pool. The weekend had lots of talks for the adults, movies and activities for the kids, and some classes for the whole family.

There was one class led by a counselor on "PTSD and the Family." She said that everybody who goes to war comes back changed—some more than others—and that it takes time to get into a new routine. She explained that anger is normal, and it's OK to feel that way. She encouraged families to take a break from discussions when things get heated up and really tense. She said that some veterans lose their cool a lot—and it's not the kids' fault.

She said we will get through this tough time. She told us to focus on the positive, do fun things together as a family, and have regular family meetings where everyone can say what they're thinking and feeling. It's good to know that other families are dealing with this stuff, too...it helps to remember we're not alone.

FEBRUARY 15

Time Alone with Dad

Dad and I have been arguing a lot again, so, like that counselor at the family weekend suggested, we decided to plan some activities together—go out to breakfast once a month (my idea ☺), mow the lawn together (his idea ☹), watch movies together for family movie night—sounds good. The time alone with Dad is what I missed the most while he was gone and during the tough times right after he got back....

Dad's been home from Iraq for 6 months now. This sure can be a slow process, but things are definitely getting better. I know he put himself in harm's way to protect my freedom and to help other countries live in peace. He'll always be my hero.

This is What I've Learned

✓ My dad has a lot to deal with from all he experienced in the war—I can see it in his face. This PTSD thing is REAL...just as real as a broken arm.

✓ Therapy really helps my dad. It takes courage for him to talk about all the bad stuff he saw over there.

✓ As for me, soccer and hanging out with my friends help me a lot.

✓ Just because my dad gets mad or is quiet doesn't mean he doesn't love me. It's not my fault when he loses control. We're working on getting along...but it takes time and work on both of our parts.

✓ Like the counselor said, it's good to look on the bright side and be positive—our family has a lot to be thankful for.

Something to
think about ...

A person who has post-traumatic stress
disorder (PTSD) has experienced a life-
threatening event and can be haunted by
it for many months and even years
afterward. If your parent (like Adam's dad) has experienced a traumatic
event or has PTSD, here are two things we want you to know:

1. Many thousands of service members are returning
   from deployment with emotional issues or PTSD—
   your family is not alone.

2. With proper care and support, most of our military
   personnel go on to lead happy, productive lives.

If your parent has PTSD, you might recognize some of the following behaviors.

People with PTSD may:

- **Re-live the trauma**
    - ✓ *Have nightmares and thoughts/memories of the event that come out of nowhere*
    - ✓ *Experience flashbacks (feel like the trauma is happening again)*
    - ✓ *Feel upset when they think about the event*

- **Avoid reminders of the trauma**
    - ✓ *Avoid places, people, and activities that remind them of the trauma*
    - ✓ *Lose interest in activities*
    - ✓ *Shut down emotionally, feel "numb," and distance from others*

- **Feel tense and "on edge" much of the time**
    - ✓ *Struggle to fall or stay asleep*
    - ✓ *Explode in anger or be irritable/crabby a lot of the time*
    - ✓ *Need to be very sure of their surroundings and may get anxious if surprised or startled*

As you saw in **Adam's** blog, reconnecting after deployment can be difficult, both for the teenager and the parent. Pick out a few of these activities and give them a try—just have fun!

Have a "movie night" at home— no phone calls, Facebook, or texting!

Stay overnight in a hotel with a pool, and order pizza

Volunteer (food shelf, nursing home, animal shelter)

Attend a local sporting event and tailgate

Pray together or read the Bible or other holy books

Start new traditions: farmer's market on Saturday mornings; chocolate-chip pancakes for Sunday breakfast

Check out the local parks and trails, and go on a family bike ride

Go to church or services at the synagogue as a family

Make dinner as a family

Coach a sports team of young kids together

Take a class together (yoga, cooking, website design, gun safety)

Discuss what gave you strength while your parent was deployed (song, poem, scripture, etc.)

Show your parent what has changed in your neighborhood while he/she was deployed

Play cards or a board game— do a puzzle together

Go to a water park—just get wet and have fun!

Carlos

Dad is in the Marines

Interests: Shooting hoops, hunting and fishing, playing baseball, chatting with friends on Facebook

I'm in Shock

I can't believe what my mom just told me. Dad has been wounded in Iraq. I don't know what happened. Something about an IED (Improvised Explosive Device) blowing up when he was on a convoy mission. I'm SO scared. My heart is going a million beats per minute, and I can't seem to calm down. I've seen people in movies and on TV who were injured, but never dreamed MY dad would get hit by an IED. I just want to see him. I have no idea how badly he's hurt. I don't even want to think about what my mom and I would do if he dies. I'm never going to be able to sleep tonight....

This is a Nightmare

I found out that Dad is in a hospital in Germany. He's in pretty bad shape, but he's going to live. I'm just freaking out, but I'm happy he's going to survive. The bomb blew his right leg off. I can't believe I'm writing this. I feel like I'm gonna puke. This can't be happening—my dad without a leg. It's like a nightmare and I can't wake up!

SEPTEMBER 3

So Far Away

Mom just called from Germany. She flew over there right after getting the news, and Grandma is staying with me. Guess Dad will stay in Germany a few more weeks and then he will be transferred to Walter Reed Hospital for a few months for physical therapy—I'm not even sure what that is. He's doing OK, I guess. Cracks jokes and stuff. I can't wait to see him. Hope I can talk to him soon.

OCTOBER 4

Got to See Dad

Just visited Dad at Walter Reed. I didn't know what to expect. I felt sick to my stomach the whole plane ride out to Washington, D.C., and didn't sleep at all the night before. I was so scared to see him in a wheel-chair. Actually, he looked pretty normal except he doesn't have a right leg. This is so weird. He was always so strong and we'd play catch and hunt and fish. Now I have no idea what we'll be able to do together. The doctors talked a lot about physical therapy—getting strong again and learning how to walk with an artificial leg. Guess a lot of people have done it—it's more than I can face right now. I just want to lock myself in my room and pretend this isn't happening.

DECEMBER 15

Shooting Hoops

Basketball tryouts were last week and I made the JV team; I think the coach liked my 3-point shot and how fast I hustle up and down the court. I like some of the other guys on the team and may even get to play in a few varsity games. I like practice and running hard—it gets my mind off what's going on at home. I'm going to the movies with some friends tonight...then out for pizza—should be fun.

DECEMBER 20

Dad Is Home

Dad's home from Walter Reed now which is good. But, he's really moody—kinda tense and jumpy. I guess he has a TBI as well as having lost his leg. The doctors at the VA hospital tell us that a TBI happens when you're so close to an explosion that your brain kind of rattles around in your head. Anyway, he forgets lots of stuff, seems really sad, and has bad headaches. I feel sorry for him—he was defending our country and our freedom, but look what happened. It's just not fair.

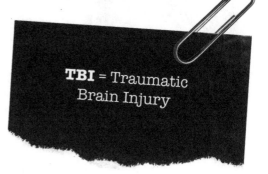

TBI = Traumatic Brain Injury

FEBRUARY 15

Valentine's Day Dance

I asked a girl from my English class (Shannon) to go to the Valentine's Day Dance with me...and she said YES! I really didn't know what she'd say because we hadn't hung out much outside of school...so I was pumped she said she'd go. Shannon looked pretty, and we ended up going as a group with a bunch of friends. The dance itself was OK—no one really danced and the music was kinda lame. The best part of the night was going out to eat afterward and having tons of waffles!!

MARCH 3

Dad Is Out of his Wheelchair

Basketball is almost over, and Dad made it to one of my last games. I played well—scored double digits—and was so glad to have him there. His physical therapy is helping, and he has a high tech artificial leg. He's learning to walk again. The doctor says he may even be able to run again—that would be great because he used to do a couple marathons every year. For now, he just feels great to be out of that wheelchair.

Mom and Dad have been arguing a lot lately. Everything is harder now, and we all get frustrated. I feel better when I go to my room and just chill out...or sometimes I get out of the house and go for a long run.

I joined the youth group at church. John, the leader, is cool and has some fun activities planned: going on mission trips, volunteering at a soup kitchen, tutoring younger kids in reading. It's nice to have an adult that I can hang out with. It helps me deal with Dad not being able to do stuff with me like he used to.

APRIL 17

People Can Be SO Rude!

I've been really messed up about everything that's going on with Dad. It's hard to see him learning to walk again. Sometimes we'll be at the mall and people will stare at his artificial leg—ugh!!

The youth leader at church could tell that something was bothering me and asked if I wanted to talk after youth group on Wednesday. So I just spilled my guts about Dad and his leg and his moods and how I just wish everything was the way it used to be. John was really cool—usually I get upset because my friends don't get what I'm going through, but John's dad is a Vietnam veteran so he understands. We prayed and talked about God's plan for all of us, and how we're never alone. I know that John is always there if I need to talk.

MAY 11

Summer Camp?

My mom just signed me up for OPC—Operation Purple Camp—a camp just for kids who have a parent in the military. I've never heard of it, but am going to check out the website. Might be good to meet other military kids....

JULY 2

Got to Meet a Three-Star General

OPC was a blast. Lots of swimming, canoeing, nature walks, camp fires, and great food. There were 8 guys in my cabin, and the leaders were pretty cool. They made camp a lot of fun. Sometimes we talked about our family and the whole deployment deal. We could all relate to being "military brats," changing schools a lot, and having to make new friends over and

over. Sometimes we just hung out and talked about our favorite movies and videogames.

The best day of camp was Military Appreciation Day. They cleared off the middle of the camp and landed a real Chinook helicopter. It was massive! We got to go aboard and look around and check out the cockpit. The pilot was there and talked to us about flying that giant. We also learned about other stuff—like how to fold the American flag and what each fold means. We tasted MREs—meals ready to eat—totally gross—especially the powdered scrambled eggs. I don't know how they eat that crap!

At night a 3-star general named Mike talked to us—he was from the Pentagon. Mike told us he was proud of OUR service—all that we sacrifice having our parent far away for so long. It's cool that the people in Washington, D.C., recognize that we serve, too! Mike asked us to be brave and strong—pretty awesome day. I can't wait to tell my dad about it.

JULY 20

Keeping In Touch

Was chatting on Facebook with some friends I met at OPC. They're really the only ones who understand what it's like to have a parent in the military. It was fun seeing pictures that they had posted on Facebook of us acting goofy at OPC—that camp was such a blast!

AUGUST 22

Rebuilding in Mississippi

It's almost the end of summer, and I'm not ready for school to start—where did the summer go? I'm going to try out for football I think. This summer we drove all the way to Mississippi for our Confirmation mission project. Had a lot of time to hang out with John on the road trip which was good. Mississippi was mega hot but it was good to rebuild a sports center in a very poor area.

SEPTEMBER 10

Making Progress

Dad is walking better each day. He hangs out at the Vet Center and talks to other vets—especially other amputees. They have counselors there, too. He and Mom seem to be getting along better. This has been hard on everyone, but things are improving slowly. I'm so glad Dad is home and alive and we're working things out. Life is different than before but it's going to be OK.

This is What I've Learned

✔ Even though Dad has been through a lot, he's still the same person inside, and I love him.

✔ Modern technology is amazing! With his artificial leg, Dad can do almost everything he did before—just a bit slower sometimes. I hope he will be able to start running again someday….

✔ Although it was Dad who got hurt, everyone in our family has been affected by it.

✔ It's good to open up to someone I can trust.

✔ Camps like OPC are great—it's good to hang out with other military kids who know where you're coming from.

✔ Sometimes life isn't fair, so you have to learn to deal with the challenges that come your way and try to be positive.

✔ It helps to relax in my room where I can get away from all the stress in my family.

Something to think about ...

Having a parent lose a limb can be stressful, so it's understandable that **Carlos** described some pretty strong emotions in his blog. Your parent has his/her own unique story and set of challenges, so you probably have experienced some intense feelings, too. When you get worked up and tense, it can help to do something relaxing.

Carlos learned that chilling out in his room and praying helped him through difficult times. Where might you find a peaceful place: In nature? In music? At home playing with your pet?

Another good thing to do when you're stressed is just to kick back and have fun! Sometimes it's helpful to forget about your family's problems and enjoy yourself. You might play videogames, listen to your iPod, text with friends, watch movies, go to the mall, hang out at the pool....What else?

Another stress-buster is to do something physical (remember Carlos' awesome 3-point shot in basketball?). Exercise is the cheapest, most effective way to deal with strong feelings. You could run, swim, take an aerobics or yoga class, lift weights at the gym, or ride a bike. What do you do?

One more thing....it always feels good to help someone else who is in a similar situation. Just like Mariah helped Kim get comfortable in the military group, you could make a difference in someone else's life. How could you help someone else today?

Meredith

One brother, Chris (14), one sister, Amanda (10), and a puppy (Luca)

Dad is in the Army

Interests: Writing, reading, listening to music, going to the mall with friends

SEPTEMBER 15

Bad Scene at Home

I hate when my parents fight. Seems like it happens all the time now. They're either yelling or totally ignoring each other. Makes me want to stay as far away from home as possible. I'm writing articles for the school newspaper. It helps to keep busy. Can't believe I'm a junior!

SEPTEMBER 25

♥ ♥ ♥

I really like this guy named Brad—he's a senior and is the editor of our school newspaper. I'm gonna start working on my articles after school when he's there—I hope we can hang out. We've been texting each other some lately which has been fun. He has a great sense of humor and makes me laugh.

OCTOBER 8

Dad Has Really Changed

Dad has been home from Afghanistan for three months now, and he seems pissed that we all did OK when he was gone. It's like he resents that we actually got along without him. What the heck! Wasn't that the idea? He's always checking up on me—where I'm going and when—now he's criticizing what I wear, as if he knows anything about my clothes. He's changed—we've changed—it's like we really don't know each other anymore. He can really blow up at all of us. His temper and how he talks to us can really hurt.

NOVEMBER 18

Life Sucks

It's hard to study at home, and the newspaper takes up a lot of time. My classes are really hard, and my grades dropped last quarter. My parents are SO angry. I'm tired all the time. Homecoming is next week and everybody is excited, but I don't have a date. I guess I'll go to the football game but that's all. I hate homecoming. I don't really care about anything right now.

JANUARY 10

Report Card Just In

Just got my report card. Mom and Dad are gonna freak out when they see all the D's and F's—especially because I used to have straight A's! I just can't seem to concentrate on anything. School just doesn't matter much anymore....

FEBRUARY 8

Forgotten

Haven't written in a few weeks—actually I haven't done much of anything in a long time. There's so much drama at home that I just stay in my room and listen to my iPod. I quit the newspaper—they didn't need me anyway, and Brad is busy with basketball so he wasn't there very much.

Dad is really freaking out—he just heard that Tom, a war buddy from Afghanistan, committed suicide last week. Dad and Tom were really close. Tom made it through the war OK, but everything he saw and did during his deployment really got to him when he got home. I sure hope my dad doesn't do something stupid like Tom did—I don't know what I'd do. As much as Dad drives me crazy lately, I still love him and need him.

I feel so alone and confused. I have no idea who to talk to. Sometimes I think nobody even knows that I exist.

FEBRUARY 16

Tell Me This Isn't Happening

OK—I can't believe it. Mom and Dad are getting a divorce. This is terrible. Now what? Where will I live? Who will I live with? Chris, Amanda, and I are freaking out. It just really sucks. I guess I should have expected it because they fought so much, but I didn't think it would ever happen to MY family!

MARCH 21

Hiding Out

My room is still the best place for me to be—I can escape and get away from everyone. I like drawing and writing my blog on the computer...it helps me to get my feelings out.

Dad moved out. Mom cries a lot, and so does Amanda. Chris seems to be in his own little world and spends a lot of time in his room. In a way it's more peaceful without Dad around. I'm trying to do everything around the house to help out, but I just can't. It's too much. Nothing seems like fun so I just hang out in my room, listen to music, and play with my puppy, Luca. I feel so down. No one calls anymore and I can't sleep. I don't understand any of this.

APRIL 6

Leave Me Alone!

One of my teachers talked to me last week about how sad I seemed, so we went to see the school counselor. Too many people are paying attention to me—I wish everyone would just leave me alone!! After talking for a while, we decided I needed to let Mom know how awful I felt. Mom was pretty cool about it, and she suggested I see my doctor. Well, I guess I've got depression—and it sucks. My first appointment with a counselor is next week—not sure I want to go—I don't know why I have to talk about my personal stuff to someone I don't even know. I really just want to be left alone.

MAY 11

Counselor Seems to Understand

I guess I'm gonna be OK. I've seen the counselor three times, and he's actually a really nice guy. He listens a lot and understands what I'm going through. He has some good ideas, too. He tells me that depression is common—that I'm not alone—it can happen to anyone, any time, anywhere. I haven't done anything wrong. There is help available and lots of kids get depressed when their parents split up. He reminded me that my family has been through a lot. I really miss my dad not being around all the time—my counselor and I are trying to figure out ways to stay in touch with him now that he moved out. I told a couple close friends about my depression and getting help. I was afraid they were going to think I was "crazy" for seeing a counselor, but they were actually really cool and understanding. I'm lucky to have such good friends.

Did you know depression is VERY common? **Depression** is more than just a bad day—it's when you feel very sad for a long time and can't do your regular activities (like school or sports).

MAY 15

Art Class

I'm taking an art class at the community college downtown to improve my drawing. It was kinda awkward at first, not knowing anybody else in the class, but I've met some nice girls and am learning a lot. I'm also running with some friends after school a couple times/week. I feel so much better afterward, and it's a great way to get in shape for summer. Won't be long before my friends and I can start hanging out at the beach!

MAY 28

Things Are Better

Dad took us to a movie last night. It couldn't be violent or about war or have too much sex—sure made it hard to find a good one! It felt good to be with Dad—he was joking around and seemed calmer.

I like my counselor and it feels good to talk to an adult about all kinds of stuff—Dad, Mom, school, Brad, college. My grades are getting better and I'm writing an article for the newspaper on what it's like to have a dad in the military. Maybe I'll submit it, maybe not.

JUNE 3

Summer Is Finally Here!

Got a job! I'm a hostess at the new Italian restaurant downtown. Fun people to work with and I love the money. I'll be able to work there all summer—maybe Brad will come in??

JULY 9

Time with Dad

Chris, Amanda, and I kind of have a regular schedule to be with Dad. Sometimes it's fun and we do cool stuff like going to the lake for the weekend—other times we just watch TV and it's boring. At least we're together though. Dad is getting counseling, too—I hope it helps. He and Mom are talking now and are at least being civil to each other. Sure glad the fighting has stopped. I see my counselor every few weeks now which helps me get through the tough days—they still happen once in a while, but much less often than before. I'm glad I'm feeling better.

SEPTEMBER 15

Senior Year

School has started and it's great to see all my friends again. I've got to take the ACT in a couple weeks and have started working on college applications—ugh! Although I like being the oldest at school, it's also a little sad because it will be the last time for everything. This year is going to FLY by! I'm the editor of the sports page in our school newspaper this year which is fun—our football team is off to a great start this season.

I feel like I've come out on the other end of this depression thing—I'm in such a better place that I was last year.

This is What I've Learned

✔ Depression can happen to anyone, any time, anywhere.

✔ If you feel really sad, talk to someone about it. I felt so much better when I stopped keeping everything to myself.

✔ There's a suicide hotline you can call any time of the night or day if you need someone to talk to. The hotline number is easy to remember—it's 1-800-SUICIDE.

✔ Counseling can help. It made a huge difference for me.

Depression is common and, as **Meredith** found out, can happen to anyone. Being a teenager is an emotional time, filled with highs and lows you never imagined. Having a parent deploy can add to the roller coaster you may feel you are riding.

Something to think about . . .

It may be helpful to take a moment to see if you may be experiencing some signs of depression. We encourage you to consider these questions:

- Do you feel very sad for days, weeks, or months at a time?

- Is it sometimes hard to do your normal activities?

- Have you withdrawn from your family and friends?

- Are you using alcohol or street drugs to escape sadness or other strong feelings?

If you've answered "yes" to any of these questions, it would be a good idea to talk to someone. Family members (parents, siblings, cousins, godparents, etc.) can be great, and they may welcome the chance to talk to you. Other people in your community may also be supportive such as your friends, parents of friends, counselors, teachers, coaches, ministers/priests/rabbis, etc. Opening up to others is always your choice, but we encourage you to use the support of people who surround you and care about you.

*"In the beginning of life, when we are infants,
we need others to survive, right?*

*And at the end of life, when you get like me,
you need others to survive, right?"*

*His voice dropped to a whisper. "But here's the secret:
in between, we need others as well."*

—Mitch Albom quoting his mentor, Morrie Schwartz,
in *Tuesdays with Morrie*

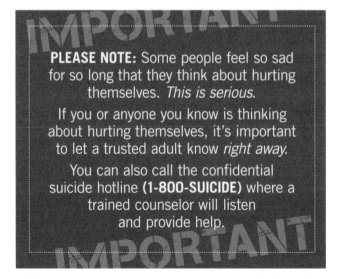

PLEASE NOTE: Some people feel so sad
for so long that they think about hurting
themselves. *This is serious.*

If you or anyone you know is thinking
about hurting themselves, it's important
to let a trusted adult know *right away.*

You can also call the confidential
suicide hotline **(1-800-SUICIDE)** where a
trained counselor will listen
and provide help.

AND NOW IT'S YOUR TURN... YOUR STORY

Now that you've read about Mariah, Adam, Carlos, and Meredith, it's time to turn to the most important person in this book...YOU!

As you read these blogs, maybe you remembered some similar experiences you and your family have had in dealing with deployment. You might have related to Mariah's loneliness, Adam's confusion and disappointment, Carlos' shock, or Meredith's depression. Reading these stories may have reminded you of the great time you had at Operation Purple Camp, the way in which your faith has grown, the pride you feel for your parent's service, or your excitement in counting the days until your parent's homecoming. Or, maybe your experience has been quite different. Anyway, this is a chance for you to write your story (don't worry about writing in complete sentences—there is no right or wrong way to do this—just write your thoughts and feelings).

It can be helpful to write about the ups and downs of being a military kid. You can create a blog like the four teens did, use the prompts we provide, or just write whatever comes into your head. Maybe you want to write a series of poems, a song, or a letter to your parent. Just find something that works for you and get started.

Now it's your turn—your chance to capture and tell your unique, important story.

You are our heroes. • *We care about you.* • *We will never forget you.*

Thank you.

Michelle and DeAnne

My STORY

My parent is in the _____
(fill in the military branch that your parent serves/served in)

Deployment and Homecoming

My parent's first tour was in _____ from _____ to _____
Location   *Dates*

My parent's second tour was in _____ from _____ to _____

My parent's third tour was in _____ from _____ to _____

How we kept in touch while my parent was gone...

_____

_____

What helped me while my parent was gone...

_____

_____

Things my parent missed while he/she was gone...

_____

_____

Other things I want to say about my parent's deployment...
(Example: how I felt while he/she was gone, who I could talk to, etc.)

_____

_____

_____

On the day that my parent got home, I...

_____

_____

Reconnecting After Deployment

Things that are going well now that my parent is home...

_____

_____

Things that are not going well or are difficult...

_____

_____

Activities my parent and I enjoy doing together...

_____

_____

I'm not the same person I was when my parent left.
Here are some ways I've changed...

_____

_____

Things I have learned about my parent...

_____

_____

I'd like my parent to know...

_____

_____

Final Thoughts

Ways in which I have grown...

_____

_____

Things I've learned about myself...

_____

_____

Communication in my family right now is....

_____

_____

I admire my parent because...

_____

_____

I admire my parent (or other relatives/friends) who took care of me while my military parent was deployed because...

_____

_____

People I can turn to when I need to talk...

_____

_____

My advice for other military kids...

_____

_____

Things I've learned...

_____

_____

GLOSSARY

Chinook helicopter: A helicopter being used in the wars in Iraq and Afghanistan, especially for air assault missions. The helicopter delivers troops into the bases and later brings supplies, food, water, and ammunition.

Counselor / therapist: A trained mental health professional who can help you and your family during difficult times.

Deployment: A military unit's move from its home base to another location—a period of time spent in a war zone.

Depression: A medical condition where you feel sad or down for long periods of time. Different from just the "blues," depression gets in the way of enjoying life, relationships, and everyday activities (school, work, etc.). Many effective treatments are available for people dealing with depression.

IED: "Improvised Explosive Device": Bombs commonly used by terrorists and often found on the side of the road. An IED explosion is one of the leading causes of death and injury in the wars in Iraq and Afghanistan.

MRE: "Meals Ready to Eat": Pre-packaged individual meals that are quick and easy to eat in a combat zone.

National Guard: A state-based military force whose members can be called on to provide assistance in a local, state, or federal emergency.

"New normal": Everyone has changed during the deployment and the old routines often don't work anymore. It takes time to create this "new normal," a new way of getting along as a family once the service member returns home.

OPC: Operation Purple Camp. Free week-long camps for military kids ages 7–17 sponsored by the National Military Family Association. For more information, please see their website: *www.operationpurple.com*

Pentagon: The headquarters of the United States Department of Defense which is located in Arlington, Virginia.

Physical therapy: A treatment to help injured people regain function after being injured— may involve learning how to walk or to use a prosthesis (an artificial limb).

PTSD: "Post-traumatic Stress Disorder": A condition that can develop after someone experiences a very upsetting event. He/she is haunted by memories of the event and may have difficulties with sleep, anger, relaxation, and getting along with others.

Suicide hotline: A phone number you can call to get immediate, confidential support and counseling. The number is easy to remember: 1-800-SUICIDE.

TBI: "Traumatic Brain Injury": Damage to the brain due to some external force such as a blast. A TBI can affect not only your physical health, but also your thinking, emotions, and behavior. Much progress has been made in helping people who have had a brain injury. Treatment and rehabilitation may include medication, surgery, physical therapy, speech therapy, and occupational therapy.

Tour of duty: A period of time spent in a combat zone—but can also describe duties at a specific location during peacetime. Tours typically last 6–15 months, depending on the mission.

VA hospital: Veterans Affairs hospital. There are over 150 hospitals and 900 outpatient clinics across the United States where veterans can get healthcare.

Vet Center: Outpatient clinics that help veterans and families by providing readjustment counseling. There are over 200 Vet Centers across the United States. Each Vet Center has at least one staff person whose job is to reach out to and support veterans from Iraq and Afghanistan.

Walter Reed Army Medical Center / Walter Reed National Military Medical Center: A large military hospital in Washington, D.C., where many seriously injured troops spend weeks to months for rehabilitation. It serves warriors from all branches of the military.

Military Youth Websites:

Guard Family Youth: National Guard Youth and Family Program: *www.guardfamilyyouth.org*

Operation Military Kids: A place for military teens to blog: *www.operationmilitarykids.org/public/stories.aspx*

The Price of Peace: Song by two military teens about their dad's deployment: *www.thepriceofpeace.org*

VA Kids: Games, activities, and information about veterans and the Veterans Affairs healthcare system for youth and teachers: *www.va.gov/kids*

Voice for the Military Child: A Military Child Education Coalition site where military teens can blog: *http://voiceforthemilitarychild.org/*

Young Heroes: Military Deployment Through the Eyes of Youth: A DVD for teens about the deployment cycle: *www.operationmilitarykids. org/public/somk.aspx*

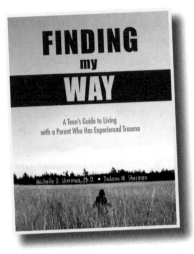

Another Helpful Resource For Military Teens:

Finding My Way: A Teen's Guide to Living with a Parent Who Has Experienced Trauma

We hope that reading about Mariah, Adam, Carlos, and Meredith reminded you that many military families face challenges before, during, and after deployment. As you saw in these blogs, everyone in the family changed while the parent was away, and each teenager had some struggles when their mom or dad returned.

Now, we'd like to offer a way to help you deal with *your* family situation. We have a great follow-up book for teens whose parents have experienced a traumatic event. *Finding My Way: A Teen's Guide to Living with a Parent Who Has Experienced Trauma* is an interactive book that can serve as a "next step" in understanding your parent's difficulties, sorting through your feelings and reactions, and learning how to get through tough times.

Finding My Way will:

✓ Provide a clear explanation of PTSD, depression, and anxiety, including some of the common symptoms and treatments.

✓ Help you figure out how to deal with anger, sadness, confusion, fear, and other strong feelings.

✓ Describe 5 common reasons why trauma survivors often turn to alcohol and drugs.

✓ Remind you who YOU can count on for support.

✓ Guide you in sorting through the pro's and con's of opening up to your friends.

✓ Describe over 25 things you can do during the rough times.

✓ Teach you ways of expressing your thoughts and feelings.

✓ Help you learn how to communicate better with people that are important to you.

✓ Provide a list of helpful books, websites, and other resources.

✓ Offer hope!

To learn more, see sample pages, or order, please see our website:

www.SeedsofHopeBooks.com

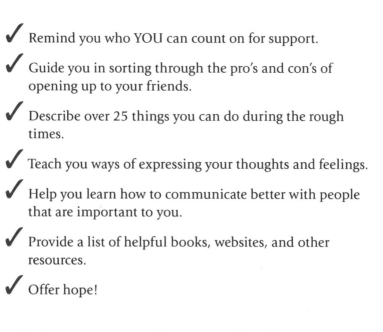

Seeds of Hope
🌷 Books™

...Where families matter

HOW TO ORDER

Resources from Seeds of Hope Books

My Story: Blogs by Four Military Teens
A series of four blogs that describes the experience of
military teens before, during, and after parental
deployment.

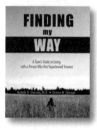

*Finding My Way: A Teen's Guide to Living with a Parent
Who Has Experienced Trauma*
An award-winning, interactive book that addresses key
issues in dealing with a parent who has experienced a
traumatic event.

*I'm Not Alone: A Teen's Guide to Living with a Parent
Who Has a Mental Illness*
Created to support the thousands of youth whose parents
have a mental illness, this interactive book focuses on the
teenager's experience of living with a parent who depression, bipolar disorder, or schizophrenia.

Order online at www.SeedsofHopeBooks.com (secure website)

Or call BookHouse Fulfillment at **(800) 901-3480**

Please call for quantity discounts